FAVOURITE
RHYMES

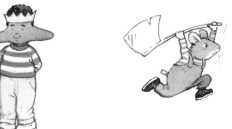

Contents

Material in this edition was previously published by Ladybird Books in the *Nursery Rhymes* gift book.

Published by Ladybird Books Ltd.
27 Wrights Lane London W8 5TZ
A Penguin Company
10 9 8 7 6 5 4 3 2

© LADYBIRD BOOKS LTD 1995
LADYBIRD and the device of a Ladybird are trademarks of Ladybird Books Ltd

Printed in Italy

Ladybird

FAVOURITE RHYMES

Chosen by RONNE RANDALL
Illustrated by PETER STEVENSON

Girls and Boys, Come Out to Play

Girls and boys, come out to play,
The moon is shining bright as day.
Leave your supper and leave your sleep,
And come with your playfellows into the street.
Come with a whoop, and come with a call,
Come with a good will, or come not at all.
Come, let us dance on the open green,
And she who holds longest shall be our queen.

Round About the Rosebush

Round about the rosebush,
    Three steps,
    Four steps,
All the little boys and girls
    Are sitting
    On the doorsteps.

Ring-a-Ring o' Roses

Ring-a-ring o' roses,
A pocket full of posies.
A-tishoo! A-tishoo!
We all fall down!

Here We Go Round the Mulberry Bush

Here we go round the mulberry bush,
    The mulberry bush, the mulberry bush.
Here we go round the mulberry bush,
    On a cold and frosty morning.

This is the way we wash our clothes,
    Wash our clothes, wash our clothes.
This is the way we wash our clothes,
    On a cold and frosty morning.

How Many Days?

How many days has my baby to play?
Saturday, Sunday, Monday,
Tuesday, Wednesday, Thursday, Friday,
Saturday, Sunday, Monday.
Hop away, skip away,
My baby wants to play,
My baby wants to play every day!

Dance to Your Daddy

Dance to your daddy,
My little babby,
Dance to your daddy,
My little lamb!

You shall have a fishy
In a little dishy,
You shall have a fishy
When the boat comes in!

Catch Him, Crow

Catch him, crow! Carry him, kite!
Take him away till the apples are ripe.
When they are ripe and ready to fall,
Here comes baby, apples and all!

Up, Up, Up

Here we go up, up, up.
And here we go down, down, down.
Here we go backwards and forwards,
And here we go round and round!

Dance, Little Baby

Dance, little baby, dance up high!
Never mind, baby, Mother is by.
Crow and caper, caper and crow,
There, little baby, there you go.
Up to the ceiling, down to the ground,
Backwards and forwards, round and round!
Dance little baby, and Mother shall sing,
With the merry chorus, ding-a-ding, ding.

To Market

To market, to market, to buy a fat pig,
Home again, home again, jiggety-jig.
To market, to market, to buy a fat hog,
Home again, home again, jiggety-jog.

This Little Pig

This little pig went to market,
This little pig stayed at home.
This little pig had roast beef,
This little pig had none.
And this little pig cried, "Wee-wee-wee,"
All the way home.

The Blacksmith

"Robert Barnes, my fellow fine,
Can you shoe this horse of mine?"
"Yes, indeed, that I can,
As well as any other man.
There's a nail, and there's a prod,
And now, you see, your horse is shod!"

Cobbler, Cobbler

Cobbler, cobbler, mend my shoe,
Get it done by half-past two.
Do it neat, and do it strong,
And I will pay you when it's done.

One, Two, Buckle My Shoe

One, two, buckle my shoe,

Three, four, knock at the door.

Five, six, pick up sticks,

Seven, eight, lay them straight.

Nine, ten, a big fat hen,

Eleven, twelve, dig and delve.

Thirteen, fourteen, maids a-courting,

Fifteen, sixteen, maids in the kitchen.

Seventeen, eighteen, maids in waiting,

Nineteen, twenty, my plate's empty.

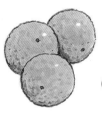

Oranges and Lemons

Oranges and lemons,
Say the bells of St Clement's.

You owe me five farthings,
Say the bells of St Martin's.

When will you pay me?
Say the bells of Old Bailey.

When I grow rich,
Say the bells at Shoreditch.

Pray, when will that be?
Say the bells of Stepney.

I'm sure I don't know,
Says the great bell at Bow.

Here comes a candle to light you to bed,
And here comes a chopper to chop off your head.

London Bridge

London Bridge is falling down,
    Falling down, falling down.
London Bridge is falling down,
    My fair lady.

Build it up with iron bars,
    Iron bars, iron bars.
Build it up with iron bars,
    My fair lady.

Iron bars will bend and break,
    Bend and break, bend and break.
Iron bars will bend and break,
    My fair lady.

Build it up with gold and silver,
    Gold and silver, gold and silver.
Build it up with gold and silver,
    My fair lady.

Gold and silver I've not got,
    I've not got, I've not got.
Gold and silver I've not got,
    My fair lady.

Then off to prison you must go,
    You must go, you must go.
Then off to prison you must go,
    My fair lady.

The Queen of Hearts

The Queen of Hearts,
She made some tarts,
All on a summer's day.
The Knave of Hearts,
He stole the tarts,
And took them clean away.

The King of Hearts
Called for the tarts,
And beat the Knave full sore.
The Knave of Hearts
Brought back the tarts,
And vowed he'd steal no more.

The Lion and the Unicorn

The Lion and the Unicorn
Were fighting for the crown.
The Lion beat the Unicorn
All around the town.
Some gave them white bread,
Some gave them brown,
Some gave them plum cake,
And drummed them out of town.

Humpty Dumpty

Humpty Dumpty sat on a wall,
Humpty Dumpty had a great fall.
    All the King's horses
    And all the King's men
Couldn't put Humpty together again.

Ride a Cockhorse

Ride a cockhorse to Banbury Cross,
To see a fine lady upon a white horse.
Rings on her fingers and bells on her toes,
And she shall have music wherever she goes.

This Is the Way the Ladies Ride

This is the way the ladies ride,
Nimble, nimble, nimble, nimble.
This is the way the gentlemen ride,
A gallop, a trot, a gallop, a trot.
This is the way the farmers ride,
Jiggety-jog, jiggety-jog.
And when they come to a hedge – they jump over!
And when they come to a slippery space –
They scramble, scramble, scramble,
Tumble-down Dick!

The Coachman

Up at Piccadilly, oh!
The coachman takes his stand,
And when he meets a pretty girl,
He takes her by the hand.
Whip away for ever, oh!
Drive away so clever, oh!
All the way to Bristol, oh!
He drives her four-in-hand.

Ride, Baby, Ride

Ride, baby, ride,
Pretty baby shall ride,
And have a little puppy dog tied to his side,
And a little pussy cat tied to the other,
And away he shall ride to see his grandmother,
To see his grandmother,
To see his grandmother.

You Ride Behind

You ride behind and I'll ride before,
And trot, trot away to Baltimore.
You shall take bread, and I will take honey,
And both of us carry a purse full of money.

Pop Goes the Weasel!

Up and down the City Road,
    In and out the Eagle,
That's the way the money goes,
    Pop goes the weasel!

Half a pound of tuppenny rice,
    Half a pound of treacle,
Mix it up and make it nice,
    Pop goes the weasel!

Bangalorey Man

Follow my Bangalorey Man,
Follow my Bangalorey Man,
I'll do all that ever I can
To follow my Bangalorey Man.

We'll borrow a horse and steal a gig,
And round the world we'll do a jig,
And I'll do all that ever I can
To follow my Bangalorey Man.

The Muffin Man

Oh, do you know the muffin man,
    The muffin man, the muffin man.
Oh, do you know the muffin man
    That lives in Drury Lane?

Oh, yes, I know the muffin man,
    The muffin man, the muffin man.
Oh, yes, I know the muffin man
    That lives in Drury Lane.

I'm a Little Teapot

I'm a little teapot,
Short and stout,
Here is my handle,
Here is my spout.
When I see the teacups,
Hear me shout,
"Tip me over and pour me out!"

Polly Put the Kettle On

Polly put the kettle on,
Polly put the kettle on,
Polly put the kettle on,
    We'll all have tea.

Sukey take it off again,
Sukey take it off again,
Sukey take it off again,
    They've all gone away.

Blow the fire and make the toast,
Put the muffins down to roast,
Blow the fire and make the toast,
    We'll all have tea.

Wash the Dishes

Wash the dishes, wipe the dishes,
Ring the bell for tea.
Three good wishes, three good kisses,
I will give to thee.

Handy Pandy

Handy Pandy, Jack-a-dandy,
Loves plum cake and sugar candy.
He bought some at the grocer's shop,
And out he came, hop, hop, hop!

Clap, Clap Handies

Clap, clap handies,
Mummy's wee one.
Clap, clap handies,
Till Daddy comes home,
Home to his bonny wee baby.
Clap, clap handies,
My bonny wee one.

Pat-a-Cake

Pat-a-cake, pat-a-cake, baker's man!
Bake me a cake as fast as you can.
Roll it and pat it and mark it with "B",
And put it in the oven for baby and me.

Five Little Mice

This little mousie peeped within,
This little mousie walked right in!
This little mousie came to play,
This little mousie ran away!
This little mousie cried, "Dear me!
Dinner is done and it's time for tea!"

Two Little Dickey Birds

Two little dickey birds sat upon a hill,
One named Jack, the other named Jill.
Fly away, Jack! Fly away, Jill!
Come again, Jack! Come again, Jill!

Dance, Thumbkin, Dance

Dance, Thumbkin, dance,
Dance, ye merry men, every one.
But Thumbkin, he can dance alone,
Thumbkin, he can dance alone.

Dance, Foreman, dance,
Dance, ye merry men, every one.
But Foreman, he can dance alone,
Foreman, he can dance alone.

Dance, Longman, dance,
Dance, ye merry men, every one,
But Longman, he can dance alone,
Longman, he can dance alone.

Dance, Ringman, dance,
Dance, ye merry men, every one,
But Ringman, he can dance alone,
Ringman, he can dance alone.

Dance, Littleman, dance,
Dance, ye merry men, every one.
But Littleman, he can dance alone,
Littleman, he can dance alone.

Incy Wincy Spider

Incy Wincy Spider climbed up the water spout.
Down came the rain and washed the spider out.
Out came the sunshine, dried up all the rain,
And Incy Wincy Spider climbed up the spout again.

25

Little Miss Muffet

Little Miss Muffet
Sat on a tuffet,
Eating her curds and whey.
There came a big spider,
Who sat down beside her,
And frightened Miss Muffet away.

Curly Locks

Curly Locks, Curly Locks, wilt thou be mine?
Thou shalt not wash dishes, nor yet feed the swine,
But sit on a cushion and sew a fine seam,
And feast upon strawberries, sugar and cream.

Little Tommy Tucker

Little Tommy Tucker
Sings for his supper.
What shall he eat?
White bread and butter.

How will he cut it
Without e'er a knife?
How will he marry
Without e'er a wife?

Little Jack Horner

Little Jack Horner sat in a corner,
Eating his Christmas pie.
He put in his thumb,
And pulled out a plum,
And said, "What a good boy am I!"

Little Betty Blue

Little Betty Blue
Lost her holiday shoe.
What can little Betty do?
Give her another,
To match the other,
And then she may walk in two.

One for the Money

One for the money,
Two for the show,
Three to make ready,
And four to go!

I Love Sixpence

I love sixpence, jolly, jolly sixpence,
    I love sixpence as my life.
I spent a penny of it, I spent a penny of it,
    I took a penny home to my wife.

I love fourpence, jolly, jolly fourpence,
    I love fourpence as my life.
I spent twopence of it, I spent twopence of it,
    I took twopence home to my wife.

I love nothing, jolly, jolly nothing,
    I love nothing as my life.
I spent nothing of it, I spent nothing of it,
    I took nothing home to my wife.

My Father, He Left Me

My father, he left me, just as he was able,
One bowl, one bottle, one table,
Two bowls, two bottles, two tables,
Three bowls, three bottles, three tables,
Four bowls, four bottles, four tables,
Five bowls, five bottles, five tables,
Six bowls, six bottles, six tables.

Hot Cross Buns

Hot cross buns!
Hot cross buns!
One a penny, two a penny,
Hot cross buns!
If your daughters do not like them,
Give them to your sons.
One a penny, two a penny,
Hot cross buns!

Four-Leaf Clover

One leaf for fame, one leaf for wealth,
One for a faithful lover,
And one leaf to bring glorious health,
Are all in a four-leaf clover.

One, He Loves

One, he loves; two, he loves;
Three, he loves, they say.
Four, he loves with all his heart;
Five, he casts away.
Six, he loves; seven, she loves;
Eight, they both love.
Nine, he comes; ten, he tarries;
Eleven, he courts; twelve, he marries.

There Were Two Wrens

There were two wrens upon a tree,
Whistle and I'll come to thee.
Another came, and there were three,
Whistle and I'll come to thee.
Another came, and there were four.
You needn't whistle any more,
For, being frightened, off they flew,
And there are none to show to you.

Two Crows

There were two crows sat on a stone,
One flew away and there was one.
The other, seeing his neighbour gone,
He flew away and then there were none.

Two Cats of Kilkenny

There once were two cats of Kilkenny,
Each thought there was one cat too many.
So they fought and they fit,
And they scratched and they bit,
Till, excepting their nails,
And the tips of their tails,
Instead of two cats, there weren't any.

Three Blind Mice

Three blind mice,
Three blind mice,
See how they run!
See how they run!
They all ran after the farmer's wife,
Who cut off their tails with a carving knife.
Did you ever see such a sight in your life,
As three blind mice?

White Feet

One white foot, buy him,
Two white feet, try him.
Three white feet, wait and see.
Four white feet, let him be.

Barber, Barber

Barber, barber, shave a pig,
How many hairs to make a wig?
Four and twenty, that's enough.
Give the barber a pinch of snuff.

Gregory Griggs

Gregory Griggs, Gregory Griggs,
Had twenty-seven different wigs.
He wore them up, he wore them down,
To please the people of the town.
He wore them east, he wore them west,
But he never could tell which he loved best.

Bobby Shaftoe

Bobby Shaftoe's gone to sea,
Silver buckles on his knee.
He'll come back and marry me,
Bonny Bobby Shaftoe!

Bobby Shaftoe's fat and fair,
Combing down his yellow hair.
He's my love forevermore,
Bonny Bobby Shaftoe!

Rub-a-Dub-Dub

Rub-a-dub-dub,
Three men in a tub,
And how do you think they got there?
The butcher, the baker,
The candlestick-maker,
They all jumped out of a rotten potato,
'Twas enough to make a man stare.

I Saw a Ship A-Sailing

I saw a ship a-sailing,
    A-sailing on the sea,
And oh, but it was laden
    With pretty things for thee.

There were comfits in the cabin,
    And apples in the hold.
The sails were made of silk,
    And the masts were made of gold.

The four-and-twenty sailors
    That stood between the decks
Were four and twenty white mice
    With chains about their necks.

The captain was a duck
    With a packet on his back,
And when the ship began to move,
    The captain said, "Quack! Quack!"

The Grand Old Duke of York

Oh, the grand old Duke of York,
He had ten thousand men.
He marched them up to the top of the hill,
And he marched them down again.
And when they were up, they were up.
And when they were down, they were down,
And when they were only halfway up,
They were neither up nor down!

The Big Ship Sails

The big ship sails on the alley, alley O,
The alley, alley O, the alley, alley O.
The big ship sails on the alley, alley O,
On the last day of September.

The captain said, "It will never, never do,
Never, never do, never, never do."
The captain said, "It will never, never do,"
On the last day of September.

The big ship sank to the bottom of the sea,
The bottom of the sea, the bottom of the sea.
The big ship sank to the bottom of the sea,
On the last day of September.

We all dip our heads in the deep blue sea,
The deep blue sea, the deep blue sea.
We all dip our heads in the deep blue sea,
On the last day of September.

Little Bird

Once I saw a little bird
Come hop, hop, hop.
So I cried, "Little bird,
Will you stop, stop, stop?"

I was going to the window
To say, "How do you do?"
But he shook his little tail,
And far away he flew.

Summer Breeze

Summer breeze, so softly blowing,
In my garden pinks are growing.
If you go and send the showers,
You may come and smell my flowers.

Mary, Mary

Mary, Mary, quite contrary,
How does your garden grow?
With silver bells and cockle shells,
And pretty maids all in a row!

Grey Goose and Gander

Grey goose and gander,
    Waft your wings together,
And carry the good King's daughter
    Over the one-strand river.

I Had a Little Nut Tree

I had a little nut tree,
    Nothing would it bear
But a silver nutmeg
    And a golden pear.

The King of Spain's daughter
    Came to visit me,
And all for the sake
    Of my little nut tree.

Old King Cole

Old King Cole was a merry old soul,
And a merry old soul was he.
He called for his pipe, and he called for his bowl,
And he called for his fiddlers three.

Each fiddler he had a fiddle,
And the fiddles went tweedle-dee.
Oh, there's none so rare as can compare
With King Cole and his fiddlers three.

Sing a Song of Sixpence

Sing a song of sixpence,
A pocket full of rye.
Four and twenty blackbirds
Baked in a pie.

When the pie was opened,
The birds began to sing.
Wasn't that a dainty dish
To set before the King?

The King was in the counting house,
Counting out his money.
The Queen was in the parlour,
Eating bread and honey.

The maid was in the garden,
Hanging out the clothes,
When down came a blackbird
And pecked off her nose!

41

Jack Be Nimble

Jack be nimble,
Jack be quick.
Jack jump over
The candlestick.

Jumping Joan

Here am I,
Little jumping Joan.
When nobody's with me,
I'm all alone.

Leg Over Leg

Leg over leg,
As the dog went to Dover.
When he came to a stile,
Hop! He went over.

Hogs in the Garden

Hogs in the garden, catch 'em, Towser.
Cows in the cornfield, run, boys, run.
Cats in the cream pot, run, girls, run.
Fire on the mountains, run, boys, run!

See-Saw, Margery Daw

See-saw, Margery Daw,
Jacky shall have a new master.
Jacky shall have but a penny a day,
Because he can't work any faster.

See-Saw, Sacra Down

See-saw, sacra down,
Which is the way to Boston town?
One foot up, the other foot down,
That is the way to Boston town.

Here Sits the Lord Mayor

Here sits the Lord Mayor,
Here sit two men.
Here sits the cock, and here sits the hen.
Here sit the little chickens,
And here they run in,
Chin-chopper,
Chin-chopper,
Chin-chopper, chin!

Round and Round the Garden

Round and round the garden,
Like a teddy bear.
One step, two steps,
Tickle you under there!

Teddy Bear, Teddy Bear

Teddy bear, teddy bear,
Turn around.
Teddy bear, teddy bear,
Touch the ground.

Teddy bear, teddy bear,
Climb the stairs.
Teddy bear, teddy bear,
Say your prayers.

Teddy bear, teddy bear,
Turn out the light.
Teddy bear, teddy bear,
Say good night.

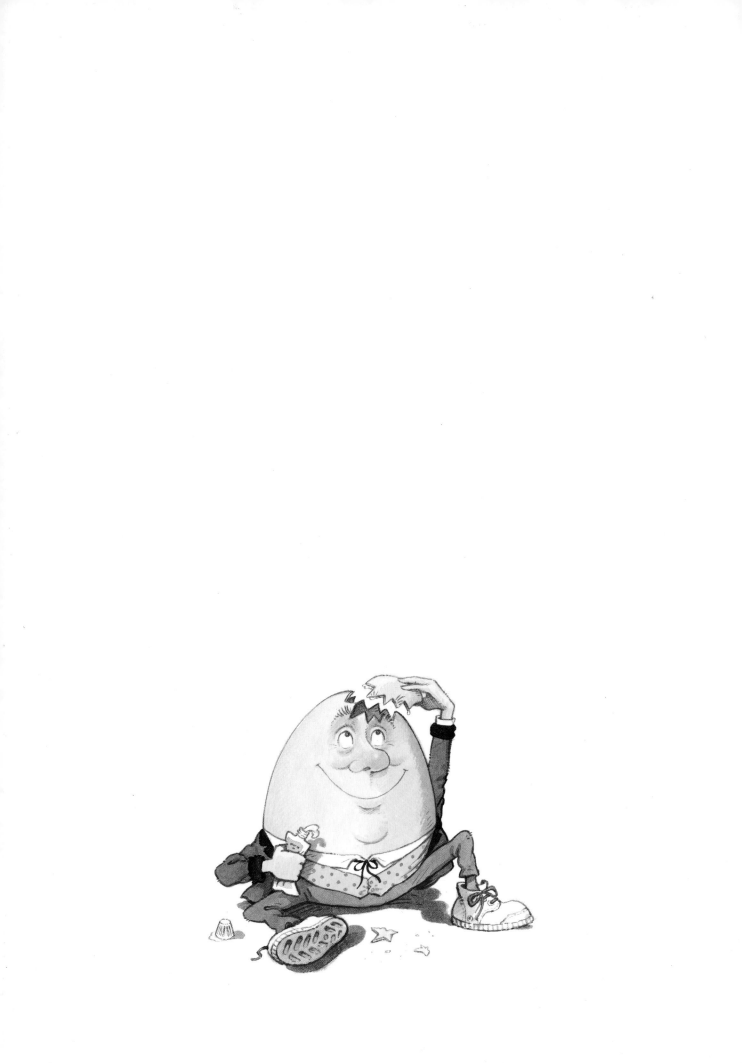